CW00383203

Simultaneou

Imran Chaki
Pratik Patel
Naisarg Pujara

Simultaneous Estimation of Cefixime and Linezolid

By HPLC Method

LAP LAMBERT Academic Publishing

Imprint

Any brand names and product names mentioned in this book are subject to trademark, brand or patent protection and are trademarks or registered trademarks of their respective holders. The use of brand names, product names, common names, trade names, product descriptions etc. even without a particular marking in this work is in no way to be construed to mean that such names may be regarded as unrestricted in respect of trademark and brand protection legislation and could thus be used by anyone.

Cover image: www.ingimage.com

Publisher:
LAP LAMBERT Academic Publishing
is a trademark of
International Book Market Service Ltd., member of OmniScriptum Publishing Group
17 Meldrum Street, Beau Bassin 71504, Mauritius

Printed at: see last page
ISBN: 978-613-9-45475-4

ACKNOWLEDGEMENT

"Nothing can be changed by changing the face but everything can be changed by facing the change......!!!! Life is yours, live it on your own principles......"

In life sometimes you never know what god decides for you, but always believe in yourself and god because this is the key of surviving in life. This is what I am thinking about the life. My thoughts toward the life give me inspiration and faith to face the difficult condition comes across in life.

Today at the end of my work, I heartly remember my family, my teachers, my friends and almighty god.

Thanks! Is a small word to my beloved parents, my brother and all my family members who not only supported me but also inspired me during the course of my work.

At the earliest, I consider this as an opportunity to express my heartfelt gratitude and sincere thanks to my esteemed guide, Prof. Dr. G. Vidya Sagar (M.Pharm., Ph.D.) Principal of Veerayatan Institute of Pharmacy for his valuable suggestions, encouragement, motivation, support, guidance and Co-operation throughout the project.

I now do use this occasion to express my heartful thanks to Dr. Meeta A. Jiladia M. Pharm. Ph.D. and Prof. Pratik S. Mehta M. Pharm Dept. of Quality Assurance. Veerayatan Institute of Pharmacy, for providing all the necessary help for my work and also for their constant support and encouragement.

1

I also express my deep gratitude to Prof. Mr. Chirag J. Patel, Mr. Ishab Paliwal, Mr. Mahesh K. Senghani, Mr. Prakash S. Sukhramani, Ms. Vaibhavi Thacker, Mr. Bhavik Sheth, Ms. Janki Ganatra, and the entire staff of Veerayatan Institute of Pharmacy for the valuable guidance during the course of study.

I extend my sincere thanks to Dr. K.R. Vadaliya Dept. of Quality Assurance, Mr. Hiren Ambasna and Kaushik Kapuriya Dept. of Pharmaceutical chemistry for their suggestions and co-operation.

I also express my sincere thanks to Mr. Parvez Bayad, Mr. Mayank Kotak, Mr.Bharat Makwana, Ms. Halima Gajan, Ms. Neeta Bhinde for helping me in my work. I express my sincere gratitude to librarian Mr. Naveen Shrimali for their valuable help.

I would like to extend my special thanks to my friends Kathiriya Rohit Sumra Basir and Radhanpuri Shagufta for their kind support, willing help, and their awesome co-operation.

Loving thanks to my dearest friends especially Dhaval, Priyank, Mayur, Ankit, Pradip, Kandarp and all my classmate. for their moral support throughout the entire project.

Finally, I don't have words to show my gratitude towards the GOD. Saying is that a leaf cannot even move without the consent of GOD then how can other things? Without the blessings of GOD, I would not be able to achieve my destination.

Thankful to all I ever remain.

Chaki Imran A

DEDICATED
TO MY BELOVED PARENTS, FAMILY
AND FRIENDS

TABLE OF CONTENTS

LIST OF FIGURES

LIST OF TABLES

CHAPTER - 1
INTRODUCTION

1. INTRODUCTION

1.1 INTRODUCTION TO HIGH PERFORMANCE LIQUID CHROMATOGRAPHY (HPLC)[1,2,3,4,5,6]

Definition

HPLC is a physical separation technique conducted in the liquid phase in which a sample is separated into its constituent components (or analytes) by distributing between the mobile phase (a flowing liquid) and a stationary phase (sorbents packed inside a column). An online detector monitors the concentration of each separated component in the column effluent and generates a chromatogram. HPLC is the most widely used analytical technique for the quantitative analysis of pharmaceuticals, biomolecules, polymers, and other organic compounds.

Principle of High Performance Liquid Chromatography: Normal-Phase Chromatography (NP HPLC)

Normal-phase HPLC explores the differences in the strength of the polar interactions of the analytes in the mixture with the stationary phase. The stronger the analyte-stationary phase interaction, the longer the analyte retention. As with any liquid chromatography technique, NP HPLC separation is a competitive process. Analyte molecules compete with the mobile-phase molecules for the adsorption sites on the surface of the stationary phase. The stronger the mobile-phase interactions with the stationary phase, the lower the difference between the stationary-phase interactions and the analyte interactions, and thus the lower the analyte retention. Mobile phases in NP HPLC are based on nonpolar solvents (such as hexane, heptane, etc.) with the small addition of polar modifier (i.e., methanol, ethanol). Variation of the polar modifier concentration in the mobile phase allows for the control of the analyte retention in the column. Typical polar additives are alcohols (methanol, ethanol, or isopropanol) added to the mobile phase in relatively small amounts. Since polar forces are the dominant type of interactions employed and these forces are relatively strong, even only 1 % v/v variation of the polar modifier in the mobile phase usually results in a significant shift in the analyte retention.

Reversed-Phase HPLC (RP HPLC or RPLC)

As opposed to normal-phase HPLC, reversed-phase chromatography employs mainly dispersive forces (hydrophobic or van der Waals interactions). The polarities of mobile and stationary phases are reversed, such that the surface of the stationary phase in RP HPLC is hydrophobic and mobile phase is polar, where mainly water-based solutions are employed. Reversed-phase HPLC is by far the most popular mode of chromatography. Almost 90% of all analyses of low-molecular-weight samples are carried out using RP HPLC. One of the main drivers for its enormous popularity is the ability to discriminate very closely related compounds and the ease of variation of retention and selectivity. The origin of these advantages could be explained from an energetic point of view: Dispersive forces employed in this separation mode are the weakest intermolecular forces, thereby making the overall background interaction energy in the chromatographic system very low compared to other separation techniques. This low background energy allows for distinguishing very small differences in molecular interactions of closely related analytes. As an analogy, it is possible to compare two spectroscopic techniques: UV and fluorescence spectroscopy. In fluorescence spectroscopy, emission registers essentially against zero background light energy, which makes its sensitivity several orders of magnitude higher than in UV spectroscopy, where background energy is very high. A similar situation is in RP HPLC, where its sensitivity to the minor energetic differences in analyte–surface interactions is very high attributed to the low background interaction energy.

Instrumentation

Typical HPLC system consists of the following main components:

Solvent Reservoirs: Storage of sufficient amount of HPLC solvents for continuous operation of the system is required. They could be equipped with an online degassing system and special filters to isolate the solvent from the influence of the environment.

Pump: This provides the constant and continuous flow of the mobile phase through the system; most modern pumps allow controlled mixing of different solvents from different reservoirs.

Injector: This allows an introduction (injection) of the analytes mixture into the stream of the mobile phase before it enters the column; most modern injectors are autosamplers, which allow programmed injections of different volumes of samples that are withdrawn from the vials in the autosampler tray.

Column: This is the heart of HPLC system; it actually produces a separation of the analytes in the mixture. A column is the place where the mobile phase is in contact with the stationary phase, forming an interface with enormous surface. Most of the chromatography development in recent years went toward the design of many different ways to enhance this interfacial contact.

Detector: This is a device for continuous registration of specific physical (sometimes chemical) properties of the column effluent. The most common detector used in pharmaceutical analysis is UV (ultraviolet), which allows monitoring and continuous registration of the UV absorbance at a selected wavelength or over a span of wavelengths (diode array detection). Appearance of the analyte in the detector flow cell causes the change of the absorbance. If the analyte absorbs greater than the background (mobile phase), a positive signal is obtained.

Data Acquisition and Control System: Computer-based system that controls all parameters of HPLC instrument (eluent composition (mixing of different solvents); temperature, injection sequence, etc.) and acquires data from the detector and monitors system performance (continuous monitoring of the mobile-phase composition, temperature, backpressure, etc.).

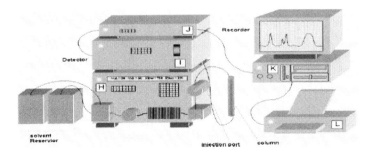

Figure 1.1: Schematic diagram of HPLC Instrument

Basic Chromatographic Descriptors

Four major descriptors are commonly used to report characteristics of the chromatographic column, system, and particular separation:

1. Retention factor (k)
2. Efficiency (N)
3. Selectivity (α)
4. Resolution (R)

1. Retention factor

Retention factor (k) is the unitless measure of the retention of a particular compound in a particular chromatographic system at given conditions and id defined as

$$k = \frac{V_R - V_0}{V_0} = \frac{V'_R}{V_0} = \frac{t_R - t_0}{t_0}$$

Where V_R is the analyte retention volume, V_0 the volume of the liquid phase in the chromatographic system, t_R the analyte retention time, and t_0 sometimes defined as the retention time of non-retained analytes.

12

Retention factor is convenient since it is independent of the column dimensions and mobile phase flow rate. Note that all other chromatographic conditions significantly affect analyte retention.

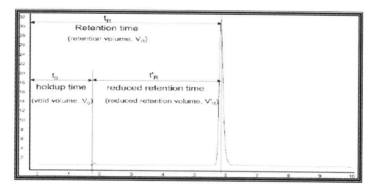

Figure 1.2: Analyte retention descriptors.

2. Efficiency

Efficiency is the measure of the degree of peak dispersion in a particular column, as such it is essentially the characteristic of the column. Efficiency is expressed as the number of theoretical plates (N) calculated as

$$N = 16\left(\frac{t_R}{w}\right)^2$$

Where tR is the analyte retention time and w the peak width at the baseline.

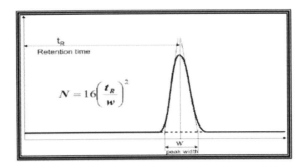

Figure 1.3: Schematic of the efficiency measurements (number of the theoretical plates in the column).

3. Selectivity (α)

Selectivity (α) is the ability of chromatographic system to discriminate two different analytes. It is defined as the ratio of corresponding capacity factors

$$\alpha = \frac{k_2}{k_1}$$

4. Resolution (R)

Resolution (R) is a combined measure of the separation of two compounds and includes peak dispersion and some form of selectivity.

Resolution is defined as

$$R = 2\frac{t_{R,2} - t_{R,1}}{w_2 - w_1}$$

Strategy for Method Development in HPLC

Everyday many chromatographers face the need to develop a high-performance liquid chromatography (HPLC) separation. Method development and optimization in liquid chromatography is still an attractive field of research for theoreticians (researchers) and attracts also a lot of interest from practical analysts. Complex mixtures or samples require systematic method development

14

involving accurate modeling of the retention behavior of the analyte. Among all the liquid chromatographic methods, the reversed phase systems based on modified silica offers the highest probability of successful results. However, a large number of (system) variables (parameters) affect the selectivity and the resolution.

HPLC method development follows a series of steps which are summarized as below:
Information on a sample, define separation goals

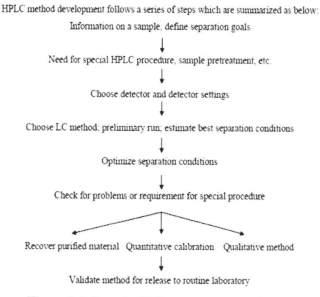

Figure 1.4: Steps in HPLC method development

HPLC method development is not very difficult when a literature reference for the same or similar compounds to be analyzed can be found, but what happens when references to the compounds of interest do not exist?

1) Nature of sample

Before proceeding with development of method for a particular sample, it is absolutely essential to have detailed information about sample. The components and excipients present should be identified. Impurity present in sample must be identified. Some important information concerning sample:

1. Number of components present.
2. Chemical structures (functionality) of compounds.
3. Molecular weights of compounds.
4. PKa values of compounds.
5. UV spectra of compounds.
6. Concentration range of compounds in samples of interest.
7. Sample solubility.

2) Separation goal

The goals of HPLC separation need to be specified clearly. Some related questions that should be asked at the beginning of method development include:

1. Is the primary goal quantitative analysis, the detection of a substance, the characterization of unknown sample components or the isolation of purified material?
2. Is it necessary to resolve all sample components?
3. If quantitative analysis is requested, what levels of accuracy and precision are required?
4. For how many different sample matrices should the method be designed?
5. How many samples will be analyzed at one time?

3) Sample pre-treatment

Sample pre-treatment is very important in development of a new method. Most of sample required dilution before injection. Samples come in various forms:

> 1. Solution ready for injection.
> 2. Solution requires dilutions, buffering, and addition of an internal standard.
> 3. Solid that must be dissolved or extracted.
> 4. Samples that require sample pretreatment to remove interference and/or to protect the column or equipment from damage.

Direct injection of the sample is preferred for its convenience and greater precession. Best result are obtained when concentration of sample solvent are same as mobile phase. Nature and concentration as samples are very important because concentrated analyte can damage the column.

4) Detector and detector settings

Before the first sample is injected during HPLC method development, we must be reasonably sure that the detector selected will sense all sample components of interest. Variable-wavelength ultraviolet (UV) detectors normally are the first choice, because of their convenience and applicability for most samples. For this reason, information on UV spectra can be an important aid for method development. UV spectra can found in the literature, estimated from chemical structures of sample components of interest, measured directly (if pure compounds are available), or obtained during HPLC separation by means of photodiode-array (PDA) detector.

5) Developing the separation
Selecting an HPLC Method and Initial Conditions

An exact recipe for HPLC method development cannot be provided because method development involves considerable trial and error procedures. The strategy recommended for choosing the experimental conditions for the first separation is explained below. Based on knowledge of sample composition and the goals of separation, the first question is: Which chromatographic method is most promising for this particular sample? We assume that HPLC has been chosen, but this decision should not be made before considering the alternatives. The first consideration when developing an HPLC method is to determine the solubility of the sample components. Knowing the nature of analyte will allow the most appropriate mode of HPLC to be selected. For the selection of a suitable chromatography method for organic compounds first Reversed-phase should be tried, if not successful, normal-phase should be taken into consideration. Given figure, there is a temptation to quickly take an appropriate column, prepare a sample and suitable mobile phase, and run it on the HPLC system. This may work with some trial and error, but the key to efficient method development is planning. Figure summarizes appropriate separation modes and mobile phases to consider for method development.

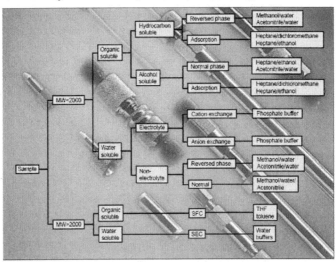

Figure 1.5: Phase Selection Process

Specifically, the experienced chromatographer will consider several aspects of the separation, as summarized in Table:

Table 1.1: Preferred Experimental Conditions for the Initial HPLC Separation

Separation Variable		Preferred initial choice
Column	Dimensions(Length × ID)	15 × 0.46 cm
	Particle Size	5μm
	Stationary Phase	C_8 or C_{18}
Mobile phase	Solvents A and B	Buffer-Acetonitrile
	% B	80-100%
	Buffer (compound, pH, concentration)	10 - 25mM Phosphate Buffer 2.0 < pH < 3.0
	Additives(e.g., amine modifiers, ion-pair reagents)	Do not use initially
	Flow-rate	1.5-2.0 ml/min
	Temperature	35 – 45°C
Sample Size	Volume	< 25 μl
	Weight	< 100 μg

Getting Started on Method Development

"Best column, best mobile phase, best detection wavelength, efforts in separation can make a world of difference while developing HPLC method for routine analysis. Determining the ideal combination of these factors assures faster delivery of desired results – a validated method of separation."

a) The Best Mobile Phase

In reverse-phase chromatography, the mobile phase is more polar than the stationary phase. Mobile phase in these systems is usually mixtures of two or more individual solvents with or without additives or organic solvent modifiers. The usual approach is to choose what appears to be the most appropriate column, and then to design a mobile phase that will optimize the retention and selectivity of the system. Separations in these systems are considered to be due to different degrees of hydrophobicity of the solutes. The polarity of organic modifier and its proportion control the rate of elution of the components in the mobile phase. The rate of elution is increased by reducing the polarity. The simple alteration of composition of the mobile phase or of the flow rate allows the rate of the elution of the solutes to be adjusted to an optimum value and permits the separation of a wide range of the chemical types. First isocratic run followed by gradient run is preferred. Since the mobile phase governs solute-stationary phase interaction, its choice is critical.

- Practical considerations dictate that it should not degrade the equipment or the column packing. For this reason, strong acids, bases and halide solutions should be avoided.
- Chemical purity of solvents is an important factor. Since large volumes of solvent are pumped through the column, trace impurities can easily concentrate in column and eventually be detrimental to the results. Spectro or HPLC grade solvents are recommended.

20

- Volatility should be considered if sample recovery is required.
- Viscosity should be less than 0.5 centipoises, otherwise higher pump pressures are required and mass transfer between solvent and stationary phase will be reduced.
- LC/MS-only volatile buffers.

b) The Best Detector

The next consideration should be the choice of detector. There is little use in running a separation if detector one uses cannot "see" all the components of interest, or conversely, if it "sees" too much. UV-visible detectors are the most popular as they can detect a broad range of compounds and have a fair degree of selectivity for some analytes. Unfortunately UV-visible detectors are not universal detectors so it is worthwhile to look at the chemical structure of the analyte to see if it has suitable chromophores, such as aromatic rings, for UV-visible detection.

Table 1.2: Summary of the some available options.

Detector	Analytes	Solvent Requirements	Comments
UV-visible	Any with chromophores	UV-grade non-UV absorbing solvents	Has a degree of selectivity and is useful for many HPLC applications
Fluorescence	Fluorescent compounds	UV-grade non-UV absorbing solvents	Highly selective and sensitive. Often used to analyze

			derivatized compounds
Refractive Index (RI)	Compounds with a different RI to the mobile phase	Cannot run mobile phase gradients	Virtually a universal detector but has limited sensitivity
Electrochemical	Readily oxidized or reduced compounds, especially biological samples	Mobile phase must be conducting	Very selective and sensitive
Evaporative Light Scattering (ELSD)	Virtually all compounds	Must use volatile solvents and volatile buffers	A universal detector which is highly sensitive. Not selective
Mass Spectrometer (MS)	Broad range of compounds	Must use volatile solvents and volatile buffers	Highly sensitive and is a powerful 2nd dimensional analytical tool. Many modes available. Needs trained operators

c) The Best Column Length

Many chromatographers make the mistake of simply using what is available. Often this is a 250 × 4.6mm C18 column. These columns are able to resolve a wide variety of compounds (due to their selectivity and high plate counts) and are common to most laboratories. While many reverse phase separations can be carried out on such column, its high resolving capabilities are often unnecessary, as illustrated in Figure 6. Method development can be streamlined by starting with shorter columns; 150, 100 or even 50mm long. This is simply because they have proportionally shorter run times.

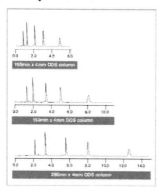

Figure 1.6: Effect of Column length

d) The Best Stationary Phase

Selecting an appropriate stationary phase can also help to improve the efficiency of method development. For example, a C8 phase (reversed phase) can provide a further time saving over a C18, as it does not retain analytes as strongly as the C18 phase. For normal phase applications, cyano (nitrile) phases are most versatile.

e) The Best Internal Diameter

By selecting a shorter column with an appropriate phase, run times can be minimized so that an elution order and an optimum mobile phase can be quickly determined. It can also be advantageous to consider the column internal diameter. Many laboratories use 4.6mm ID columns as a standard, but it is worth considering the use 4.6mm ID columns as an alternative. These require only 75% of the solvent flow that a 4.6mm column uses. This translates to a 25% solvent saving over the life of the column and can be even more significant if a routine method is developed for such a column.

f) Gradient Programming

The fastest and easiest way to develop a method is to use a mobile phase gradient. Always start with a weak solvent strength and move to a higher solvent strength. To begin, use a very fast gradient (e.g.10 minutes) and then modify the starting and finishing mobile phases to achieve a suitable separation. Of course the choice of solvents and buffers may need to be modified during method development. (Different HPLC instruments will give different results for the same gradient, so if a method is to be validated for use by several different laboratories, isocratic methods are recommended). Optimizing the mobile phase for an analysis will help to improve the separation. A number of factors depend upon the solvents chosen.

g) Retention

Analytes may be too strongly retained (producing long run times). If this occurs, the solvent strength should be increased. In reverse phase analysis this means a higher % of organic solvent in the mobile phase.

h) Poor Separation

Analytes often co-elute with each other or impurities. To overcome this, the analysis should be run at both higher and lower solvent strengths so the best separation conditions may be determined. Varying solvents may help - try methanol instead of acetonitrile for reversed phase analysis. Using buffers and modifying the pH (within the column's recommended pH range) can also assist the separation. When the optimum conditions have been achieved, improving the resolution is often just a case of changing to a longer column and/or one with a smaller particle size to increase the column efficiency. (For reversed phase analysis, having started with a 100mm C_8 column there is also the option of trying C_{18} columns to get better resolution. The important point is having used a short column for this stage of the development a lot of time was saved).

i) Peak Shape

This is often a problem, especially for basic compounds analyzed by reversed phase HPLC. To minimize any potential problems always use a high purity silica phase such as Wakosil II. These modern phases are very highly deactivated so secondary interactions with the support are minimal. Buffers can be used effectively to give sharp peaks. If peak shape remains a problem, use an organic modifier such as triethylamine, although this should not be necessary with modern phases like Wakosil. One point often forgotten is the effect of temperature changes on a separation. To maximize the reproducibility of a method, it is best to use a column heater to control the temperature of the separation. A temperature of $35 - 40°C$ is recommended.

j) Buffer selection

In reverse phase HPLC, the retention of analytes is related to their hydrophobicity. The more hydrophobic the analyte, the longer it is retained. When an analyte is ionized, it becomes less hydrophobic and, therefore, it retention decreases. When separating mixtures containing acid and/or bases by reversed phase HPLC, it is necessary to control the pH of mobile phase using appropriate buffer in order to achieve reproducible results. When separating acids and bases a buffered mobile phase is recommended to maintain consistent retention and selectivity. A buffered mobile phase, by definition, resists changes in pH so that the analytes and silica will be consistently ionized, resulting in reproducible chromatography. If the sample is neutral, buffers or additives are generally not required in the mobile phase. Acids or bases usually require the addition of a buffer to the mobile phase. For basic or cationic samples, "less acidic" reverse-phase columns are recommended and amine additives for the mobile phase may be beneficial. Optimum buffering capacity occurs at a pH equal to the pKa of the buffer. Beyond that, buffering capacity will be inadequate. Buffers play an additional role in the reproducibility of a separation. The buffer salts reduce peak tailing for basic compounds by effectively masking silanols. They also reduce potential ion-exchange interactions with unprotonated silanols (Figure 1.11). To be most effective, a buffer concentration range of 10 - 50 mM is recommended for most basic compounds.

Table 1.3: Commonly used Buffers for reversed phase HPLC

Buffer	p^{Ka} (25°C)	Maximum Buffer Range	UV Cutoff (nm)
TFA	0.3	-	210
Phosphate,p^{K}_1 H_2PO_4	2.1	1.1-3.1	< 200
Phosphate,p^{K}_2 HPO_4^{2-}	7.2	6.2-8.2	< 200
Phosphate,p^{K}_3 PO_4^{3-}	12.3	11.3-13.3	< 200
Citrate. p^{K}_1 $C_3H_5O(COOH)_2(COO)^{1-}$	3.1	2.1-4.1	230
Citrate. p^{K}_2 $C_3H_5O(COOH)_1(COO)^{2-}$	4.7	3.7-5.7	230
Citrate. p^{K}_3 $C_3H_5O(COO)^{3-}$	6.4	4.4-6.4	230
Carbonate, p^{K}_1 HCO_3^{1-}	6.1	5.1-7.1	< 200
Carbonate. p^{K}_2 CO_3^{2-}	10.3	9.3-11.3	> 200
Formate	3.8	2.8-4.8	210
Acetate	4.8	3.8-5.8	210
Ammonia	9.3	8.3-10.3	200
Borate	9.2	8.2-10.2	N/A
TEA	10.8	9.8-11.8	< 200

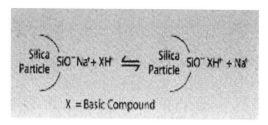

Figure 1.7: Peak Tailing Interaction

k) Selection of pH

The pH range most often used for reversed-phase HPLC is 1 - 8 and can be divided into low pH (1 - 4) and intermediate pH (4 - 8) ranges. Each range has a number of advantages. Low pH has the advantage of creating an environment in which peak tailing is minimized and method ruggedness is, maximized. For this reason, operating at low pH is recommended. At a mobile phase pH greater than 7, dissolution of silica can severely shorten the lifetime of columns packed with silica-based stationary phases.

The pKa value (acid dissociation [ionization] constant) for a compound is the pH at which equal concentrations of the acidic and basic forms of the molecule are present in aqueous solutions. Analytes may sometimes appear as broad or tailing peaks when the mobile phase pH is at, or near, their pKa values. A more rugged mobile phase pH will be at least 1 pH unit different from the analyte pKa. This shifts the equilibrium so that 99% of the sample will be in one form. The result is consistent chromatography. Dramatic changes in the retention and selectivity (peak spacing) of basic and acidic compounds can occur when the pH of the mobile phase is changed. This is often a result of different interactions between the column and the analytes when the ionization of these compounds changes. It is important to evaluate these changes when a method is developed in order to select the mobile phase pH that provides the most reproducible results.

1.2 INTRODUCTION TO METHOD VALIDATION[7,8]

Method validation is the process of documenting or proving that an analytical method provides analytical data acceptable for the intended use. The need to validate a method and the procedure to be followed are matters of professional judgment, although fairly well-prescribed procedures and guidelines are now available that aid in decision making. According to that the various validation parameters to validate each and every above stated method are:

Accuracy
Precision (repeatability and reproducibility)
Linearity and range
Selectivity/ Specificity
Robustness/ Ruggedness
Limit of detection (LOD)/ Limit of quantification (LOQ)
Stability and system suitability studies

Accuracy

The accuracy of an analytical method is the closeness of test results obtained by that method to the true value. In case of the assay of a drug in a formulated product, accuracy may be determined by application of the analytical method to synthetic mixtures of the drug product components to which known quantities of the analyte have been added (i.e. "to spike"). Accuracy is calculated as the percentage of recovery by the assay of the known added amount of analyte in the sample, or as the difference between the mean and the accepted true value, to gather with confidence intervals. Dosage form assays commonly provide accuracy within 3-5% of the true value.

The ICH documents recommend that accuracy should be assessed using a minimum of nine determinations over a minimum of three concentration levels, covering the specified range (i.e. three concentrations and three replicated of each concentration).

Precision

The precision of an analytical method is the degree of agreement among individual test results when the method is applied repeatedly to multiple samplings of a homogeneous sample. It is usually expressed as the standard deviation or relative standard deviation (coefficient of variation) of a series of measurements.

Precision may be a measure of either the degree of reproducibility or of repeatability of the analytical method. Reproducibility refers to the use of the analytical procedure in different laboratories, or on different days or with different analysts. Repeatability refers to the use of the analytical procedure within the same laboratory over a short period of time using the same analyst with the same equipment.

Precision is determined by assaying a sufficient number of samples using standard deviation or coefficient of variation for set of n value. The RSD values are important for showing degree of variation expected when the analytical procedure is repeated several time in a standard situation. (RSD below 1% for built drugs, RSD below 2% for assays in finished product).

$$RSD = \sigma \frac{(x_1 - x)^2}{(N-1)}$$

Where, σ = standard deviation

X_1 = value of each observation

x = mean value

N = number of observations

The ICH documents recommend that repeatability should be assessed using a minimum of 9 determinations covering the specified range for the procedure (i.e. 3 concentrations and 3 replicates of each concentration).

Linearity and Range

The linearity of an analytical method is its ability to elicit test results that are directly or by a well-defined mathematical transformation, proportional to the concentration of Analyte in samples within a given range. The range of an analytical method is the interval between the upper and lower levels of analyte (including these levels) that has been demonstrated to be determining with a suitable level of precision, accuracy and linearity using the method as written. The range is expressed in the same units as test results (eg. Percent, parts per million) obtained by analytical method.

Selectivity and Specificity

Specificity is the ability to assess unequivocally the analyte in the presence of components that may be expected to be present, such as impurities, degradation products, and matrix components.

If an analytical procedure is able to separate and resolve the various components of a mixture and detect the analyte qualitatively the method is called selective. On the other hand, if the method determines or measures quantitatively the component of interest in the sample matrix without separation, it is said to be specific.

Hence one basic difference in the selectivity and specificity is that, while the former is restricted to qualitative detection of the components of a sample, the latter means quantitative measurement of one or more analytes.

Selectivity may be expressed in terms of the bias of the assay results obtained when the procedure is applied to the analyte in the presence of expected levels of other components, compared the results obtained when the procedure is applied to the analyte in the presence of expected levels of other components, compared to the results obtained on the same analyte without added substances. When the other components are all known and available, selectivity may be determined by comparing the test results obtained on the analyte with and without the addition of the potentially interfering materials. When such components are either unidentified or unavailable, a measure of selectivity can often be obtained by determining the recovery of a standard addition of pure analyte to a material containing a constant level of the other components.

Robustness and Ruggedness

The robustness of an analytical method is a measure of its capacity to remain unaffected by small but deliberate variation in method parameters and provides an indication of its reliability during normal usage. The determination of robustness requires that methods characteristic are assessed when one or more operating parameter varied.

The ruggedness of an analytical method is the degree of reproducibility of test results obtained by the analysis of the same samples under a variety of normal test conditions such as different laboratories, different analysts, using operational and environmental conditions that may differ but are still within the specified parameters of the assay. The testing of ruggedness is normally suggested when the method is to be used in more than one laboratory. Ruggedness is normally expressed as the lack of the influence on the test results of operational and environmental variables of the analytical method.

For the determination of ruggedness, the degree of reproducibility of test result is determined as function of the assay variable. This reproducibility may be compared to the precision of the assay under normal condition to obtain a measure of the ruggedness of the analytical method.

Limit of Detection and Limit of Quantification

The limit of detection (LOD) is the lowest amount of analyte in a sample that can be detected, but not necessarily quantified, under the stated experimental conditions. It is usually expressed as the concentration of analyte in the sample. The determination of the limit of detection of instrumental procedures is carried out by determining the signal-to-noise ratio by comparing test results from the samples with known concentration of analyte with those of blank samples and establishing the minimum level at which the analyte can be reliably detected. A signal-to-noise ratio of 2:1 or 3:1 is generally accepted. The signal-to-noise ratio is determined by dividing the base peak by the standard deviation of all data points below a set threshold. Limit of detection is calculated by taking the concentration of the peak of interest divided by three times the signal-to-noise ratio. Other approaches depend on the determination of the slope of the calibration curve and the standard deviation of responses as shown below:

$$LOD = 3.3 \times \frac{SD}{S}$$

Where, SD = standard deviation of the response,

S = slope

The limit of quantification (LOQ) is the lowest amount of analyte in a sample that can be determined with acceptable precision and accuracy. It is usually expressed as the concentration of analyte in the sample.

It can be determined by comparing measured signals of samples with known low concentrations of analyte with those of blank samples. The minimum concentration at which the analyte can reliably be quantified is established. A typical acceptable signal- to- noise ratio is 10:1. Other approaches depend on the determination of the slope of the calibration curve and the standard deviation of responses.

$$LOQ = 10 \times \frac{SD}{S}$$

Where, SD = standard deviation of the response,

S = slope

System suitability test

System suitability tests are an integral part of liquid chromatography. These tests include tests for resolution (RS), number of theoretical plates (N)and tailing factor (T_f).

Resolution (RS)

Resolution is function of number of theoretical plates (N) and is specified to ensure that closely eluting compounds are resolved from each other.

It is determined by analyzing standard solution under stated chromatographic conditions and calculated using following equation,

$$R_S = 1.18 \, (t_{R2} - t_{R1}) / (W_{h1} + W_{h2})$$

Where, t_{R1} = Retention time of first peak

t_{R2} = Retention time of second peak

W_{h1}= Peak width of first peak at half height

W_{h2}= Peak width of second peak at half height

Number of theoretical plates (N)

It is a measure of peak sharpness which is important for detection of trace components.

t is determined by using following equation,

$$N = 5.54 (t_R/W_h)^2$$

Where, t_R = Retention time of peak

W_h = Peak width at half height

Asymmetry factor (As) or Tailing factor (Tf)

Asymmetry factor/tailing factor, a measure of peak asymmetry, is unity for perfectly symmetrical peaks and its value increases as tailing becomes more pronounced.

A_s peak asymmetry increases, integration and hence precision become less reliable. It is calculated using following equation,

$$A_S (T_f) = W_{0.05} / 2d$$

Where, $A_S (T_f)$ = Asymmetry factor (Tailing factor)

$W_{0.05}$ = Peak width at 5 % peak height

d = Half of peak width at 5% peak height

Data elements required for assay validation:

There are various analytical methods used for the examination of pharmaceutical materials. Not all the characteristics referred above will need to be considered in all cases. Analytical methods may be broadly classified in different categories differently as per WHO and as per USP. Following is the classification according to USP.

Category I: Analytical methods for quantification of major components of bulk drug substances or active ingredients including preservatives in finished pharmaceutical products.

Category II: Analytical methods for determination of impurities in bulk drugs or for determination of degradation compounds in finished pharmaceutical products.

Category III: Analytical methods for determination of performance characteristics (e.g. dissolution, drug release).

Category IV: Identification tests.

CHAPTER - 2
DRUG PROFILE

2. DRUG PROFILE

2.1 CEFIXME[9,10]

Table 2.1: Drug profile of cefexime

Identification	
Name	**Cefixime**
IUPAC Name	(6R,7R)-7-[(2Z)-2-(2-amino-1,3-thiazol-4-yl)-2-[(carboxymethoxy)imino]acetamido]-3-ethenyl-8-oxo-5-thia-1-azabicyclo[4.2.0]oct-2-ene-2-carboxylic acid
Structure	
Categories	Antibacterial.
Molecular Wt.	453.44g/mole
Chemical Formula	$C_{16}H_{15}N_5O_7S_2$
Melting Point	218-225 °c

Solubility	soluble in methanol, dimethyl sulfoxide, glycerine, and propyleneglycol.
Metabolism	Hepatic
Half life	3-4 hrs
Protein binding	65%
Toxicity	Diarrhea Nausea Vomiting

All Beta-lactam antibiotics, cefixime binds to specific penicillin-binding proteins (PBPs) located inside the bacterial cell wall, causing the inhibition of the third and last stage of bacterial cell wall synthesis. Cell lysis is then mediated by bacterial cell wall autolytic enzymes such as autolysins; it is possible that cefixime interferes with an autolysin inhibitor.

Brand names:

Cefixoral

Cefspan

Cephoral

Suprax

Therapeutic Indication:

Uncomplicated Gonorrhea

Urinary tract infection

Acute bronchitis

2.2 LINEZOLID[9,10]

Table 2.2: Drug profile of Linezolid

Identification	
Name	**Linezolid**
IUPAC Name	N-{[(5S)-3-[3-fluoro-4-(morpholin-4-yl)phenyl]-2-oxo-1,3-oxazolidin-5-yl]methyl}acetamide
Structure	
Categories	Anti-Infective Agents Protein Synthesis Inhibitors Antibacterial Agents
Molecular Wt.	337.35 g/mol

Chemical Formula	$C_{16}H_{20}FN_3O_4$
Melting Point	178-182^{0}C
Solubility	Slightly soluble → In methanol Soluble → Chloroform
Metabolism	Linezolid is primarily metabolized by oxidation of the morpholine ring, which results in two inactive ring-opened carboxylic acid metabolites: the aminoethoxyacetic acid metabolite (A), and the hydroxyethyl glycine metabolite
Half life	4.5-5.5hr
Protein binding	33%
Toxicity	Ataxia vomiting Tremors

Linezolid is a synthetic antibacterial agent of the oxazolidinone class of antibiotics. It has in vitro activity against aerobic Gram positive bacteria, certain Gram negative bacteria and anaerobic microorganisms. It selectively inhibits bacterial protein synthesis through binding to sites on the bacterial ribosome and prevents the formation of a functional 70S-initiation complex. Specifically, linezolid binds to a site on the bacterial 23S ribosomal RNA of the 50S subunit and prevents the formation of a functional 70S initiation complex, which is an essential component of the bacterial translation process.

Brand names:

Linezlid

Zyvox

Zyvoxid

Therapeutic Indication:

For the treatment of bacterial infections caused by susceptible strains of vancomycin resistant enterococcus faecium, staphylococcal aureus (methicillin resistant and susceptible strains), streptococcus pneumoniae, streptococcus pyogenes, streptococcus agalactiae.

CHAPTER - 3
LITERATURE REVIEW

3. LITERATURE REVIEW

3.1 Literature review for cefixime

Table 3.1: Reported methods for cefixime

Sr. No.	Method	Description	Ref. No.
1	Reverse phase HPLC method for the determination of cefixime in pharmaceutical dosage forms.	Column: C_{18} (250*4.6mm) Mobile phase: acetonitrile, methanol, 0.5 % ammonium acetate. (44:16:4) Flow rate: 0.8 ml/min Detection: 215nm	11
2	Kinetic spectrophotometric method for the estimation of cefixime in pharmaceutical formulations	Solvent used as distilled water	12
3	A simple and sensitive RP-HPLC method for simultaneous estimation of cefixime and ofloxacin in combined tablet dosage form	Column: C_{18}(150 *4.6 mm) Mobile phase: Methanol 0.025 mm, potassium dihydrogen phosphate buffer (70:30). Detection : 290nm	13
4	Analytical method development and validation	Column: C_{18} Inertsil Mobile phase :	14

| | of cefixime and dicloxacillin tablets by RP-HPLC | potassium hydroxide buffer and acetonitrile (60:40 v/v) Flow rate: 1.0 ml/min Detection: 220nm | |
| 5 | Simultaneous spectrophotometric estimation of cefixime and azithrhomycin in tablet dosage form | Solvent used methanol λ_{max} of Cefixime: 289.0 nm λ_{max} of azithromycin: 254.0 nm | 15 |

3.2 Literature review for Linezolid

Table 3.2: Reported methods for linezolid

Sr. No.	Method	Description	Ref. No.
1	Method development and validation of linezolid in bulk and formulation using UV spectro-photometric method	Solvent: acetonitrile Detection: 253 nm	16
2	A validated RP-HPLC method for the determination of linezolid in pharmaceutical dosage forms	Column: C_{18} (250*4.6mm) Mobile phase: acetonitrile and water (60:40)	17

		Flow rate: 1 ml/min Detection: 254nm	
3	A validated RP-HPLC method for estimation of linezolide infusion.	Column: C_{18} (150*4.6mm) Mobile phase : acetonitrile and ortho-phosphoric buffer pH (3.4) (20:80) Flow rate: 1 ml/min Detection: 251 nm	18

3.3 Literature review for cefixime and linezolid

Table 3.3: Reported method for combination

Sr. No.	Method	Description	Ref. No.
1	Method development and validation of spectrophotometric methods for simultaneous estimation of cefixime trihydrate and linezolid in their combined tablet dosage form	Solvent: methanol Detection: 288.72 nm (λ_{max} of cefixime trihydrate) and 256.70nm (λ_{max} linezolid)	19

CHAPTER - 4
AIM AND OBJECTIVE

4. AIM AND OBJECTIVE

The combined tablet dosage forms of cefixime and linezolid are commonly use and available in market for treatment of urinary tract, typhoid fever and lower respiratory tract infection anti-bactarial use due to patient compliance.

On literature survey, it was found that individually of these drugs have been analyzed by many methods, and only UV spectrometric method have been reported for the simultaneous determination of this combination. Therefore it was thought of interest to develop and validate analytical methods for the simultaneous estimation of these drugs by HPLC.

Therefore, the objective is to develop and validate simple, precise, accurate HPLC Method for simultaneous estimation of cefixime and linezolid in combined tablet dosage form.

CHAPTER - 5
PLAN OF WORK

5. PLAN OF WORK

To develop and validate analytical method for estimation of cefixime and linezolid in solid oral dosage form.

- ➢ Selection of Mobile Phase

- ➢ Optimization of Mobile Phase

- ➢ Development of Precise method

- ➢ Validation of developed method

CHAPTER - 6
EXPERIMENTAL WORK

6. EXPERIMENTAL WORK

6.1 Identification & Solubility Study of Drug

6.1.1 Experimental

➢ **Instrumentation**

- Melting Point Apparatus: Micro Controller Based Melting Point Apparatus, Chemiline, Model-CL-726
- FT-IR: Model- Shimadzu 8400 Series, (Shimadzu, Japan)

➢ **Materials**

- Linezolid Active Pharmaceutical Ingredient (API) was supplied by Windlas Biotech as gift sample.
- Cefixime Active Pharmaceutical Ingredient (API) was supplied by Aurabinda Pharma as gift sample.

6.1.2 Identification by Melting Point Determination

Melting point of linezolid and cefixime have been determined using Micro controller Based Melting Point Apparatus. The melting points of the compounds were taken by open capillary method.

Table 6.1: Melting point of drugs

Drug Name	Reported (°C)	Observed (°C)
Linezolid	112°-115°C	113°-115°C
Cefixime	218°-225°C	220°-224°C

Observation: The Melting point of cefixime and linezolid complies with that of the Standard value.

6.1.3 Identification by FTIR Spectroscopy

6.1.3.1 Linezolid

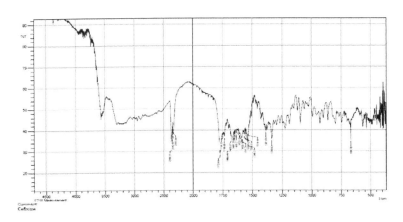

Figure 6.1: IR Spectra of linezolid

Table 6.2: IR spectra interpretation of linezolid

Sr. No.	Peak (cm^{-1})	Functional Group
1	1712.67	Acid (-C=O)
2	735	C-F Stretching
3	1640	-C=O (Amide)
4	1200	C-O Stretching
5	1150	C-N Stretching
6	1075	C-C Stretching

6.1.3.2 Cefixime

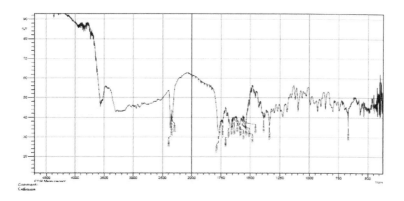

Figure 6.2: IR Spectra of cefixime

Table 6.3: IR spectra interpretation of cefixime

Sr. No.	Peak(cm^{-1})	Functional Group
1	1680	N-C=O (Amide)
2	1605	C=N
3	1755	C=O (Ester)
4	1240	C-O Stretching
5	1150	C-N Stretching
6	1000-1050	C-C Stretching

5.1.4 Solubility Study

The solubility of linezolid and cefixime were practically determined: Solubility was determined by taking 100 mg of linezolid and cefixime in 100 mL volumetric flasks, adding required quantity of solvent at room temperature and shaken for few minutes. Solubility data for each study was observed and recorded in Table 6.4.

Table 6.4: Solubility Data of Linezolid and cefixime

Solvent	Solubility	
	Linezolid (Observed)	Cefixime (Observed)
Water	Insoluble	Insoluble
Methanol	Soluble	Soluble
0.1 N HCl	Soluble	Soluble
0.1 N NaOH	Insoluble	Insoluble

Apparatus and Instruments

- Double beam UV-visible spectrophotometer (Shimadzu, model 1700) having two matched quartz cells with 1 cm light path.
- Electronic analytical balance: Acculab
- Volumetric flask – 10, 25, 50, 100 mL
- Pipettes – 1, 2, 5, 10 mL
- All instruments and glass wares were calibrated.

Reagents and Materials

- Linezolid (Windlas Biotech)
- Cefixime (Aurabinda Pharma)

- Methanol AR (Finar Chemical)

Spectophotometric Conditions
- Mode: Spectrum
- Scan speed: Medium
- Wavelength range: 400-200 nm
- Absorbance scale: 0.00A – 4.00A
- Initial base line correction: Methanol AR

6.2 Determination of Wavelength for Measurement

1 mL of working standard solution of LIN (100µg/mL) and CEF (100 µg/mL) was diluted to 10 mL with methanol to get 10µg/mL solution of both.

Each solution was scanned between 200-400 nm. Wavelengths were selected from the overlain spectra of LIN and CEF.

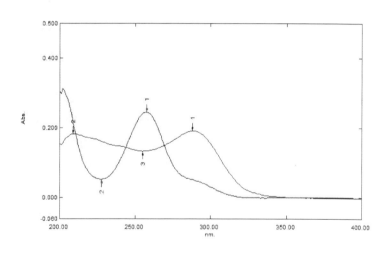

Figure 6.3: Overlain spectrum of 10 ppm LIN and 10 ppm CEF

6.3 Development and validation of stability indicating RP-HPLC method for simultaneous estimation of Linezolid and Cefixime in tablet dosage form Apparatus and Instruments

- A Shimadzu HPLC instrument (Analytical CXTH-3000) [software LC Solution, equipped with prominence diode array detector (SPD-M20A), Auto-sampler]
- An analytical balance (Sartorius analytical balance)
- pH meter (Tornado digital pH meter)
- Photostability Chamber (TH-90S, Thermolab, Mumbai, India)
- Hot air oven (TO-90S, Thermolab)
- Sonicator (Electrolab)
- Volumetric flask – 10, 50, 100 mL
- Pipettes – 1, 2, 5, 10 mL

Reagents and Materials:

- Linezolid (Windlas Biotech Ltd.)
- Cefixime (Aurbinda Pharma Ltd.)
- Combined tablet formulation (ZIFITURBO) was procured from local market.
- Acetonitrile and Methanol (HPLC grade, Finar Chemicals Ltd, Ahmedabad, India); Triethylamine and Water (HPLC grade, RFCL limited, New Delhi, India)
- Potassium dihydrogen phosphate buffer
- AR grade ortho phosphoric acid (S.D Fine Chemicals Ltd, Mumbai, India)
- Whatman filter paper no. 41. (Whatman International Ltd., England)

Preparation of 0.05M potassium buffer

Accurately weighed 3.4 g of potassium dihydrogen ortho phosphate and transferred in to 500 mL beaker. Transferred 500 mL distilled water into the beaker. pH adjusted to 6 with Potassium hydroxide.

Preparation of the mobile phase

Accurately measure and transfer the volumes as Potassium buffer: Methanol (40:60 v/v) and pH is adjusted to 3.5 by triethylamine which was filtered through 0.451 μm filter (Millipore) and degassed in ultrasonic bath prior to use.

Preparation of Standard Solution

Preparation of Standard Stock of LINEZOLID:

Accurately weighed quantity of Linezolid 100 mg was transferred into 100 mL volumetric flask, dissolved and diluted up to mark with methanol. This will give a stock solution having strength of 1000 μg/mL.

Preparation of Working Standard Solution of LINEZOLID: (W$_1$)

100 μg/mL of Linezolid solution was prepared by diluting 1 mL of stock solution to 10 mL with methanol.

Preparation of Standard Stock Solution of CEFIXIME: (S$_2$)

Accurately weighed quantity of cefixime 100 mg (equivalent to 100 mg of CPD) was transferred into 100 mL volumetric flask, dissolved and diluted up to mark with methanol. This will give a stock solution having strength of 1000 μg/mL.

Preparation of Working Standard Solution of Cefixime: (W₂)

100 μg/mL of cefixime solution was prepared by diluting 1 mL of stock solution in 10 mL with methanol.

Sample preparation: (Lable claim: Each tablet contains cefixime 200mg and linezolide 600mg)

Solution (1): Weigh and powdered 20 tablets. Weight equivalents to 10mg of cefixime and dissolve with mobile phase into 100ml volumetric flask. (Cefixime 100 mcg/ml and linezolide 300 mcg/ml)

Solution (2): Take 1ml of solution (1) and dilute with mobile phase in to a 10 ml volumetric flask (Cefixime 10 mcg/ml and linezolide 30 mcg/ml).

6.3.1 Selection and optimization of Chromatographic condition

Proper selection of the HPLC method depends upon the nature of the sample (ionic or ionizable or neutral molecule), its molecular weight and solubility. Reversed phase HPLC was selected for the initial separations because of its simplicity and suitability. To optimize the chromatographic conditions the effect of chromatographic variables such as mobile phase, pH, flow rate and solvent ratio were studied and the chromatographic parameters such as asymmetric factor, resolution and column efficiency were calculated. The condition was chosen that gave the best resolution, symmetry and column efficiency was selected for estimation.

Selection of column

For RP-HPLC method, various columns are available but our main aim is to resolve both drugs in the presence of excipients. So the C-18 column was selected for estimation of both drugs. Hypersil BDS C-18 (250mm, 4.6mm, 5μm) column was chosen to give good peak shape and high resolution, which also provides high peak symmetry, good retention for drug and facilitates the separation of drug without the interference of excipients within short run time.

Selection of mobile phase

Mobile phase consisting of Potassium Dihydrogen Phosphate Buffer (3.0 pH): MeOH (40:60), at a flow rate of 1.0 ml/min, was found to be satisfactory to obtain well-resolved peaks with better reproducibility and repeatability for Eletriptan.

Table 6.5: Trials for optimization of mobile phase for RP-HPLC method for linezolid & cefixime

SR NO.	COLUMN	MOBILE PHASE	REMARK
1	C18	Water:Methanol (50:50)	Cefixime peak was not obtained till 25min.
2	C18	Water:Methanol (40:60) pH:3.5 by TEA	Cefixime peak was not obtained till 15min.
3	C18	0.05M Potassium dihydrogen Phosphate buffer :Methanol(50:50) pH:3.5 by TEA	Peak shape is not proper
4	C18	0.05M Potassium dihydrogen Phosphate buffer :Methanol(50:50) pH:3.5 by TEA	Peak is separated and proper in shape

➤ Trial chromatogram of linezolid & cefixime

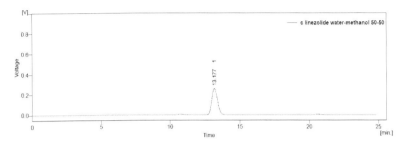

Figure 6.4: Trial 1 chromatogram of linezolid & cefixime.

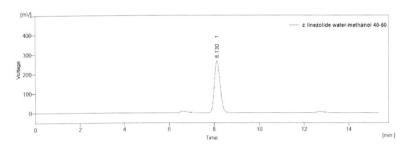

Figure 6.5: Trial 2 chromatogram of linezolid & cefixime.

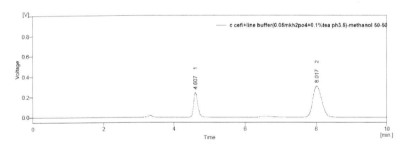

Figure 6.6 Trial 3 chromatogram of linezolid & cefixime

Optimized Chromatographic Condition

- ✓ **Stationary phase:** C18 (10 mm ×4.6 mm, 2.6 µm particle size).
- ✓ **Mobile phase:** 0.05M Potassium dihydrogen Phosphate buffer:Methanol (40:60 v/v).
- ✓ **pH:** pH of mobile phase was adjusted 3.5 with TEA.
- ✓ **Flow rate:** 1 ml/min.
- ✓ **Detection wavelength:** 277 nm
- ✓ **Total run time:** 10 min.
- ✓ **Injection volume:** 20 µl

Chromatogram of combined drug

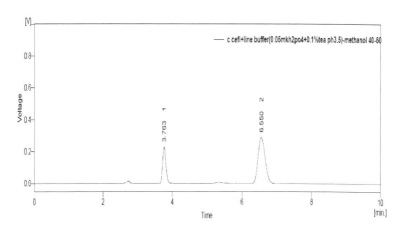

Figure 6.7: Trial 4 chromatogram of linezolid & cefixime.

Procedure

Inject separately diluent, standard and sample preparation in single into the chromatograph, record the chromatograms and measure the response for the analyte peak.

Calculate % LC by using following formula.

$$\text{ASSAY (\% LC) of OLME} = \frac{AT}{AS} \times \frac{WS}{DS} \times \frac{DT}{WT} \times \frac{Avg.wt}{LC} \times \frac{P}{100} \times 100$$

$$\text{ASSAY (\% LC) of AMLO} = \frac{AT}{AS} \times \frac{WS}{DS} \times \frac{DT}{WT} \times \frac{Avg.wt}{LC} \times \frac{408.88}{567.06} \times \frac{P}{100} \times 100$$

Where,

AT = Peak area of sample injection

AS = Peak area of standard injection

WS = Weight of working standard taken in mg

WT = Weight of sample taken in mg

DS = Dilution of standard

DT = Dilution of sample

LC = Label claim

P = Percentage purity of working standard

6.3 Analytical Method Validation

Validation was done as per ICH guideline Q2 (R1). The developed RP-HPLC methods were validated with respect to parameters such as

Validation Parameters

✓ System suitability

✓ Specificity

  • Interference from placebo

✓ Linearity

✓ Precision

  • Repeatability

  • Intermediate precision

✓ Accuracy

✓ Robustness

✓ Solution stability

System suitability

System suitability was performed by preparing the system suitability solution as per the test method, should be performed and checked before performing any parameter for used to verify that the system are adequate for the analysis intended. The parameters used in this test were retention time, theoretical plate, tailing factor, resolution. The values of system suitability results obtained were recorded in table 6.6. The Chromatograms of the same are given in figure 6.8.

Acceptance criteria

➤ % RSD of five replicate standard injections should not be more than 2.0.

➤ Theoretical Plates for the analyte peak should not be less than 2000.

➤ Tailing factor for the analyte peak should not be more than 2.0.

Table 6.6: System suitability parameter

Result	Cefixime	Linezolid
Retention Time	3.76 min	6.55 min
Theoratical plates	6896	4626
Tailing factor	1.32	1.28

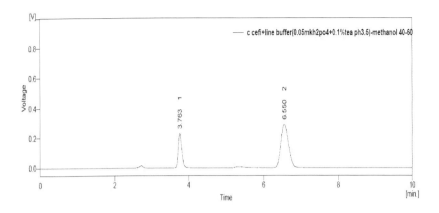

Figure 6.8: chromatogram of linezolid & cefixime.

Specificity

Specificity of an analytical method is its ability to measure the analyte accurately and specifically in the presence of component that may be expected to be present in the sample matrix.

Interference from blank and placebo

A blank preparation, standard preparation, placebo preparation, sample preparation were prepared and injected. Observed for any interference from placebo at the retention time of the analyte peak.

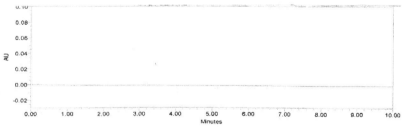

Figure 6.9: Chromatogram of diluent.

63

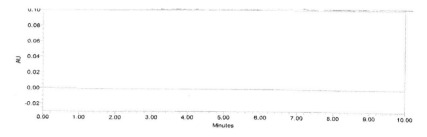

Figure 6.10: Chromatogram of placebo (1x).

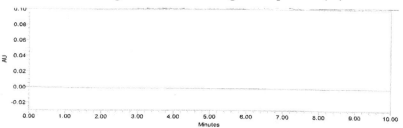

Figure 6.11: Chromatogram of placebo (3x).

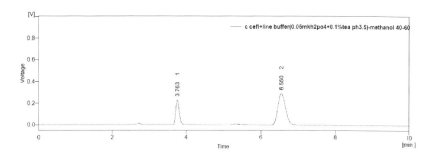

Figure 6.12 chromatogram of sample.

Linearity

The linearity study was carried out for both drugs at five different concentration levels. The linearity of Cefixime and Linezolide was in the range of 5-15 µg/mL and 15-45 µg/mL respectively. Each solution was injected under the operating chromatographic conditions. Calibration curves were constructed by plotting peak areas versus concentrations, and the regression equation was calculated. Each response was average of five determinations. The values of linearity results obtained were recorded in table. The Chromatograms of the same are given in figure.

Acceptance criteria
➢ The correlation coefficient value should not be less than 0.999.

Table 6.7: Data for linearity and range

Sr. No.	Concentration (µg/ml)		Area	
	Cefixime	Linezolide	Cefixime	Linezolide
1	5	15	827.958	2245.764
2	7.5	22.5	1168.066	3168.47
3	10	30	1525.435	4138.005
4	12.5	37.5	1896.272	5144.172
5	15	45	2266.684	6149.136

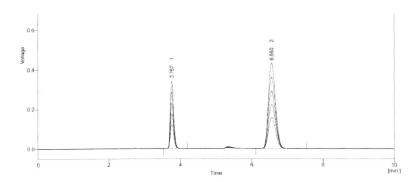

Fig 6.13: Overlain chromatogram of cefixime and linezolide.

65

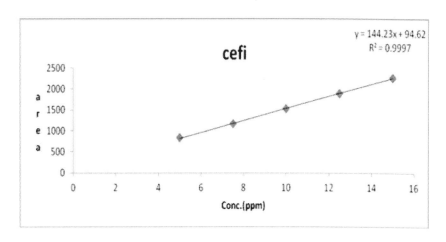

Figure 6.14: Calibration curve for cefixime.

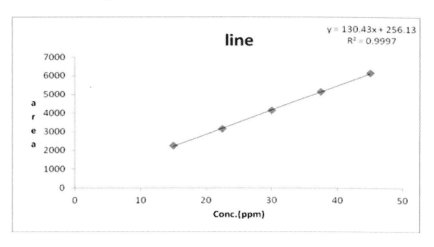

Figure 6.15 Calibration curve for linezolide.

Accuracy

The accuracy of the test method was demonstrated by preparing recovery samples. (i.e., spiking placebo with known quantities of API) at level of 50%, 100%, 150%, of target concentration. Prepare the recovery samples in triplicate in each level. The values of recovery results obtained were recorded in table.

Acceptance Criteria

> The recovery at each level should be between 98.0% - 102.0% with % RSD should not be more than 2.0.

Table 6.8: Accuracy data for estimation of cefixime and linezolide

Drug	Amount taken (μg/mL)	Amount added (μg/mL)	Amt. recovered Mean ± S.D (n=3) (μg/mL)	% recovery
Cefixime	10	8	8±0.5836	100.14
	10	10	9.97±0.1051	99.81
	10	12	11.99±0.4228	99.95
Linezolide	30	15	15.02±0.5454	100.19
	30	18.75	18.74±0.3665	99.99
	30	22.5	22.6±1.1799	100.47

Percentage recovery for cefixime was 99.81-100.14 % and for linezolide it was 99.99 – 100.47 %. The results are shown in Table 6.8.

6.8.4 Precision

Repeatability

The repeatability was checked by repeatedly (n = 6) injecting Eletriptan sample solutions and recording the responses. Determine the assay of these samples and evaluate the precision of the method by computing the % RSD of the assay results. The values of Repeatability results obtained were recorded in table.

Acceptance criteria

➤ % RSD for assay of 6 Preparation is NMT 2.0

Table 6.9: Data showing repeatability

SR. No.	Area	
	Cefixime	Linezolid
1	1510.184	4096.8
2	1508.666	4092.678
3	1502.13	3988.356
4	1514.672	4099.45
5	1511.164	4089.375
6	1509.46	3991.486
Mean	1509.379	4059.691
SD	4.1209	54.1622
% RSD	0.27	1.33

Intermediate precision

The procedure followed for method precision was repeated on a different day, by a different analyst, using a different HPLC system. Individual assay values, mean assay value and % RSD were calculated and recorded in table.

Acceptance criteria

➤ % RSD for six preparations for intermediate precision should not be more than 2.0.

Intraday precision

The data for intraday precision for cefixime and linezolid is shown in table 5.5. The % R.S.D. for Intraday precision was found to be 0.32-0.50 for cefixime and 0.84-1.73 for linezolid.

Table 6.10: Result of Intraday precision (RP-HPLC Method)

	Cefixime			Linezolid		
Conc.	Amount found ± S.D	% RSD	Conc.	Amount found ± S.D.	% RSD
5	4.86 ± 0.023	0.47	15	14.45 ± 0.2514	1.73
10	9.78 ± 0.0321	0.32	30	29.15 ± 0.4707	1.61
15	15.10 ± 0.0763	0.50	45	45.02 ± 0.3781	0.84

Interday precision

The data for inter day precision for cefixime and linezolid is shown in table 5.6. The % R.S.D. for interday precision was found to be 1.06-1.63 for cefixime and 0.63-1.60 for linezolid.

Table 6.11: Result of interday precision (RP-HPLC Method)

Cefixime			Linezolid		
Conc.	Amount found ± S.D	% RSD	Conc.	Amount found ± S.D.	% RSD
5	4.88 ± 0.0519	1.06	15	14.42 ± 0.2311	1.60
10	9.93 ± 0.1300	1.30	30	29.69 ± 0.1882	0.63
15	15.16 ± 0.2400	1.63	45	45.29 ± 0.3637	0.80

LOD and LOQ

The limit of detection (LOD) is the lowest amount of analyte in a sample that can be detected, but not necessarily quantified, under the stated experimental conditions. It is usually expressed as the concentration of analyte in the sample.

Calibration curve was repeated for five times and the standard deviation (SD) of the intercepts was calculated. Then LOD and LOQ were calculated as follows: - LOD=3.0 * SD/slope of calibration curve LOQ=10 * SD/slope of calibration curve SD = Standard deviation of intercepts

Table 6.12: LOD & LOQ for estimation of cefixime and linezolid

Cefixime		Linezolid	
LOD	LOQ	LOD	LOQ
0.27 µg/mL	0.82 µg/mL	0.81 µg/mL	2.47 µg/mL

Robustness

The robustness was studied by analyzing the sample Eletriptan by deliberate variation in the method parameters. The change in the response of Eletriptan was noted. Robustness of the method was studied by changing pH by±0.2, Organic phase ratio by ±2, flow rate by ±10% and pH by ±0.2. The effect of changes observed on system suitability parameters were recorded in table.

Robustness of proposed RP-HPLC method was carried out by changing different parameters. The method was found robust as % RSD for different robustness parameters was 1.26 for cefixime and 1.67 for linezolid. (Acceptance criteria % RSD ≤ 2)

Acceptance criteria

➢ Number of theoretical plates for the analyte peak should not be less than 2000.

➢ Asymmetry value for the analyte peak should not be more than 2.0.

➢ % RSD for 5 replicate injections for the analyte peak should not be more than 2.0 %.

Table 6.13: Robustness for estimation of cefixime and linezolid

Condition	Variation	Cefixime		Linezolid	
		%ASSAY	%RSD	%ASSAY	%RSD
Temp.	35°C	98.26		98.39	
(30 ± 5°C)	25°C	100.68		101.86	
Flow rate	0.8 ml/min	98.04	1.26	98.58	1.67
(1±0.1 ml/min)	1.1 ml/min	100.74		101.86	
pH (3.5 ± 0.2)	pH 3.3	98.39		98.69	
	pH 3.7	99.91		100.94	

Table 6.14: Analysis of marketed formulation

Formulation	Label claim (mg)		Amount found (mg)		% assay±S.D	
	Cefixime	Linezolid	Cefixime	Linezolid	Cefixime	Linezolid
Tablet	200	600	198.62	611.16	99.31 ± 0.11	101.86 ± 0.88

6.4 Summary

Table 6.15: Summery of validation parameter

Sr. no.	Parameters	Cefixime	Linezolid
1	Linearity Range	5-15 µg/mL	15-45 µg/mL
2	Correlation coefficient (R^2)	0.9997	0.9997
3	Accuracy (% recovery), n=3	99.81-100.14 %	99.99-100.47 %
4	Precision (% R.S.D) 1.Repetability (n=6) 2.Intraday precision(n=3) 3.Interday precision(n=3)	0.27 % 0.32-0.50 % 1.06-1.63 %	1.33 % 0.84-1.73 % 0.63-1.60 %
5	Limit of Detection	0.27 µg/mL	0.81 µg/mL
6	Limit of Quantitation	0.82 µg/mL	2.27 µg/mL
7	Robustness (% R.S.D)	0.50 %	0.69 %
8	Assay	99.31 % ± 0.1296	101.86 % ± 0.0093

CHAPTER - 7
CONCLUSION

7. CONCLUSION

❖ RP-HPLC method have been developed to determine cefixime and linezolid simultaneously in their combined tablets.

❖ Method was validated successfully as per ICH-recommended guidelines. The method were found to be precise as %RSD values of assay determined by these methods were less than 2.0.

❖ High percentage recoveries obtained in RP-HPLC method indicate that the methods are accurate.

❖ RP-HPLC method were found to be simple, rapid and sensitive.

❖ There was no interference from any excipients in the determination of drugs in Tablets which indicates the methods are specific.

❖ Hence, developed method can be employed for routine quality control Analysis of the combined tablet dosage form of cefixime and linezolid.

CHAPTER - 8
REFERENCES

8. REFERENCES

1. Kazakevich Y, Lobrutto R. HPLC for Pharmaceutical Scientists, John Wiley & Sons Inc, New jersey, 2007, pp 3-25.

2. Snyder LR, Kirkland JL, Glajch JL. Practical HPLC Method Development, Wiley, New York, 1997. pp 34-39.

3. Ahuja S, Rasmussen H. HPLC Method Development for Pharmaceuticals, Elsevier, Academic Press, London, 2007. pp 44-54.

4. How do I Develop an HPLC Method? Technical Article. 2001. http://www.sge.com/uploads/db/Rl/dbr/y8NOG4YTZB2MDHivmfg/Ta-0010-h.pdf

5. Valko K, Snyder LR, Glajch J. Retention in reversed-phase liquid chromatography as a function of mobile phase composition. Journal of Chromatography A. **1993**, 656(1-2), 501-520.

6. Neue UD. HPLC Columns: Theory, Technology, and Practice. John Wiley & Sons, New York, 1997, pp 926-936.

7. International Conference on Harmonization of Technical Requirements for Registration of Pharmaceuticals for Human use. Validation of Analytical Procedures: Text and Methodology ICH Q2 (R1). 2005.

8. Indian Pharmacopoeia. Vol-I. 2.4 Physical and Physiochemical Methods. Government of India, Ministry of Health & Family Welfare. Published by Indian Pharmacopoeia Commission. 2007, pp 129-30.

9. Drug Bank, Cefixime. Updated On 19April 2012. Available from http://www.drugbank.ca/cefixime/DB00601

10. Drug Bank, linezolid. Updated On 14 February2012. Available from http://www.drugbank.ca/linezolid/DB00601

11. Khaja Pasha, Patil, C.S, K. Vijaykumar, Ali, Sadath, V. B. Chimkod Reverse phase HPLC Method for the Determination of Cefixime in Pharmaceutical Dosage Forms. Research Journal of Pharmaceutical, Biological and Chemical Sciences. **2010**; 1(3): 226.

12. Ashok Kumar, Lalit Kishore, Nair Anroop, Kaur Navpreet, Kinetic spectrophotometric method for the estimation of cefixime in pharmaceutical Formulations. Der Pharma Chemical. **2011**; 3(4): 279-291.

13. Khandagle Kapil S, Gandhi Santosh V, Deshpande Padmanbh B, Gaikwad Nilesh V. A simple and sensitive RP-HPLC Method for simultaneous estimation of cefixime and ofloxacin in combined Tablet Dosage Form. International Journal of Pharmacy and Pharmaceutical sciences. **2011**; 3(1).

14. Kathiresan K, Murugan R., Hameed, M.S.Inimai, K.G. And Kanyadhara T. Analytical Method Development and validation of Cefixime and Dicloxacillin Tablets by RP-HPLC. Rasayan Journal of Chemical. **2009**; 2(3): 588-592.

15. Magar S. D, Tupe A. P, Pawar P. Y, Mane B.Y. Simultaneous spectrophotometric estimation of cefixime and azithromycin in tablet dosage form. Current Pharma Research, **2012**; 2(3): 535-538.

16. P. Vanitha, Amala Mateti, P. Prashanthi, Manish Kumar Thimmaraju, N. Raghunandan. Method development and validation of linezolid in bulk and formulation using UV spectrophotometric method. Journal of Scientific Research in Pharmacy. ISSN 2247-9469.

17. K. Jayaprasanti, B. Syamasundar. A validated RP-HPLC method for the determination of linezolid in pharmaceutical dosage forms. International Journal of Pharmacy and Bio sciences, ISSN 0975-6299.

18. Gurav Gaur, Vipin Kukkar, Ramaniranjan Singh. A validated RP-HPLC method for estimation of linezolide infusion. International Journal of Pharmaceutical Research and Development. **2012**; 4(1): 132-135.

19. Shah Helly, Patel Payal, Patel Khushbu, Solanki Sagar. Method development and validation of spectrophotometric methods for simultaneous estimation of cefixime trihydrate and linezolid in their combined tablet dosage form. International journal of pharmacy and bio sciences. 1(5): 516-519.

Printed in Great Britain
by Amazon

87556618R00052